Children's
Adventure
Theatre

Three Plays to Stage and Perform

Robin Hood

Jungle Book

Captain Hook

the last date

Terri Wiltshire

Heinemann

Children's Adventure Theatre
was produced for Heinemann Children's Reference
by Cedarwood Press/Pinpoint Design

First published in Great Britain in 1996 by Heinemann Children's
Reference, an imprint of Heinemann Educational Publishers,
Halley Court, Jordan Hill, Oxford, OX2 8EJ,
a division of Reed Educational & Professional Publishing Ltd.

MADRID ATHENS PARIS
FLORENCE PORTSMOUTH NH CHICAGO
SAO PAULO SINGAPORE TOKYO
MELBOURNE AUCKLAND IBADAN
GABORONE JOHANNESBURG KAMPALA NAIROBI

Editor: Joanna Swinnerton
Design: The Pinpoint Design Company
Photographer: Rex Caves
Illustrations by: Mike Walsh
Make-Up Artists: Isobel Staff & Julie Puddy
Costume: Rosemary Forsyth & Margaret Winters
Production Controller: Lorraine Stebbing

ISBN 0 600 58359 7 (HBK)
     0 600 58360 0 (PBK)

British Library Cataloguing-in-Publication Data.
A catalogue record for this book is available from
the British Library.

Printed in Italy

The publishers would like to thank Truly Scrumptious model
agency and the staff and children of class three, St Leonards
V & A School, Leighton Buzzard, especially their teacher Mrs
Nicholls and Headmistress Mrs Price.

Also we gratefully acknowledge prop donations by Texas,
Leighton Buzzard/Dillamore, Leighton Buzzard, Sue Breen
and Bob Portway.

NOTE: Only use water-based face paints and make-up.
Children with sensitive skin should use all make-up and
face paint with caution.

Many of the photographs in this book show children with
bare feet. Do not perform barefoot on wet, dirty or oth-
erwise dangerous surfaces.

CONTENTS

ROBIN HOOD

JUNGLE BOOK

CAPTAIN HOOK

Welcome to the theatre! You may have seen a play before, and you may even have been in a play at school. But have you ever put on a play yourself? It takes a lot of time and work, but it's a lot of fun, too.

'But I don't like acting.'

Even if you don't like acting, there are lots of things you can do – you need more than actors to put on a play. Here are some of the things you can do.

The Director
Every play needs a DIRECTOR, who chooses and directs the actors and stage crew when they REHEARSE – this is when you practise the play.

The Stage Crew
The STAGE CREW help to prepare and put on the play. Here are some of the things the stage crew can make:

Each actor needs a COSTUME, and someone has to make these, and help the actors to put them on. They can also help the actors to put on their MAKE-UP.

The actors use PROPS on stage, such as wands and crowns; someone has to make these, and keep an eye on them during the play, to make sure they are ready when the actors need them.

You may need to make STAGE FURNITURE, like cupboards and tables, and someone has to move them on and off the stage during the play.

If your play has SOUND EFFECTS, such as the sound of a galloping horse, someone has to make those noises off-stage.

If you have LIGHTS and CURTAINS for your stage, someone must operate them at the right time.

A PROMPT sits backstage with a copy of the play, and if the actors forget their words, the prompt whispers the first word or two to help them.

MAKE-UP

Actors need make-up on stage, as they will look very pale without it. Use either theatrical water-based face paints, or ordinary make-up.

1 Spread some pink blusher on your cheeks on and under the cheekbone to make them rosy.

2 Cover your eyelids with light brown or blue eyeshadow. Brush your eyelashes with mascara.

3 Put some lipstick on your lips – and you're ready for the stage!

'How do we start?'

1. Decide which play you want to put on. There are three to choose from in this book. Each play has a CAST LIST, a list of all the people in the play. If you have too many actors, some of them can be EXTRAS. Extras appear on-stage but don't have any lines to say, such as party guests and palace guards.

2. Choose someone to be the director. The director tells the actors and stage crew what to do at the rehearsal.

3. Decide who is going to play which part. The director organizes an AUDITION, which is when everyone reads aloud parts of the play and agrees which they want to play.

4. The stage crew decide what they want to do. Look in the section for your play called Costumes and Props to see what costumes, props, stage furniture and sound effects you need.

5. Let your family and friends know you are putting on a play. You could make posters and tickets to tell people when and where it is. Make sure you show the name of the play and the day, time and place where it will be performed.

NEXT! The stage crew can begin to set up the THEATRE, and make the props and costumes.

READING A SCRIPT

Reading a SCRIPT is very different from reading an ordinary story. A script is made up of two parts:

● the actors' LINES. These are the words that each character says.

● the STAGE DIRECTIONS. These tell the actor when and where to enter (appear on the stage) and when to exit (leave the stage). They also tell you how to act when you say your lines. For example, if you're supposed to be angry, you could change your voice or wave your fist in the air.

Jim: Where are you going?
Tom: To the haunted house on Mill Street. Want to come?
Jim: *(looking frightened and shaking his head)* No!
Tom: *(laughing)* What's the matter? Chicken?
Jim EXITS LEFT, angrily.

Sometimes the stage directions will tell you to say your lines OFF-STAGE. This means you are hidden in the wings and the audience can hear you speak but they can't see you.

You must listen for your CUE so that you know when it is time to say your lines. A cue is what happens just before it is your turn to speak or move. It could be a sound, like someone screaming or a doorbell ringing, or it could be another actor's words, such as 'Here she comes'.

'We don't have a theatre – so how can we put on a play?'

The Theatre
You don't need a real theatre to put on a play. A theatre can be a patio, your garage, or your living room.

You need three main areas:
1. The STAGE – a place to act;
2. The WINGS – where the actors stand when they're not on-stage so that the audience can't see them;
3. The AUDITORIUM – where the audience sits.

The Stage
You can make a curtain to go across the front of the stage by draping an old sheet or blanket over a rope or clothes-line attached to something sturdy.

The Wings
These go either side of the stage. There are various ways of making wings. Stack cardboard boxes at the sides of the stage; or put up more curtains; or use ready-made screens if you have them.

The Auditorium
All you need is lots of chairs, and perhaps a row of cushions at the front, if some people don't mind sitting on the floor. Make sure that the chairs and cushions are placed so that everyone can see clearly.

Stage Furniture
Sometimes you can use the furniture from your home, and sometimes you can make it yourself. For example, for 'Captain Hook', you will need sails, treasure chests, a sign saying 'splash' and a plank of wood.

Scenery
You may need some scenery for your stage. The easiest way to do this is to make some FLATS. To make flats, take several large sheets of cardboard and tape them together. Paint on them the scene that you want, such as bricks to show a stone wall, or trees to show a forest. Tape cardboard boxes against the back to make them stand up.

Props and Costumes
You may need a trumpet or magic wand, or a basket of fruit. You might find some of the props around your house, but if not, you can make them. Each play tells you what props you need and how to make them. If your character needs a special costume or make-up, make sure you try it out a day or two before the performance, so you can alter it if necessary.

Sound Effects, Lights and Curtains
The stage crew should read through the play to find out what sounds they need to make, and what they need to make them. They should also learn when the lights and curtains must be operated.

NEXT! The actors and stage crew practise what to do – this is called rehearsing.

'How do we learn what to say and do on the stage?'

1. At the first rehearsal, all the actors read the play aloud a few times to get used to the story and their lines. This is called a READ-THROUGH. Think about your character and how they should move and talk, and what expressions they have. Read the section on page 5 about how to read a script.

2. The director will tell you where to stand or sit or walk when you are on stage. Remember these STAGE DIRECTIONS and carry them out at each rehearsal.

3. The only way to learn your LINES is to practise, practise, practise! You can't learn all of your lines right away, so in the beginning you can read from the script.

4. Once you know your lines, practise several times without the script. The PROMPT will help you if you forget.

5. While the actors rehearse their lines, the STAGE CREW rehearse when to make the sound effects and when to operate lights and curtains.

6. Before the performance, have a DRESS REHEARSAL. This is when you perform the whole play with everything in place – props, sound effects, lights, make-up and costumes – to make sure that everyone knows what they're doing.

NEXT! It's time for the opening night!

Hints for Actors

1. Don't turn your back to the audience – they won't be able to hear you.
2. Always speak loudly and clearly, but don't shout.
3. Don't stand in front of other actors.
4. Don't talk when you are backstage, unless you are supposed to be saying a line off-stage.
5. If something goes wrong, and you forget your words or drop something, don't worry – keep going! Pretend it was meant to happen and carry on.

7

ROBIN HOOD
THE STORY

Before the first rehearsal, read through the script on your own so that you know the story. If you are acting a part, think about the character of the person you play and the best way of showing it.

Act 1

In the forest, Robin Hood fights a duel with a strange boy. He discovers that the boy is actually Maid Marian, who has come for his help. She wants Robin to save a stable-boy who helped her to escape from the sinister Sheriff of Nottingham. Robin agrees and they make a plan which involves Maid Marian going back to the Sheriff's castle.

Act 2

Soon afterwards another stranger, Friar Tuck, enters the forest. After Robin's men tie him up, he explains that he has been ordered to sing at the marriage of the Sheriff and Maid Marian. The Friar doesn't like the Sheriff, and Robin persuades him to help them in their plot.

LITTLE JOHN
A good-natured man, who enjoys joining in Robin's adventures.

ROBIN HOOD
A brave and charming outlaw, who helps the weak and the poor by stealing from the rich and outsmarting the Sheriff of Nottingham.

WILL SCARLET
One of Robin's men, Will is very suspicious of strangers and can be very stubborn.

CAST LIST

- ★ Robin Hood
- ★ Will Scarlet
- ★ Little John
- ★ Maid Marian
- ★ Friar Tuck
- ★ Sheriff of Nottingham
- ★ Stable-boy
- ★ Robin's band of men
- ★ Wedding guests
- ★ Sheriff's guards (several to guard the wedding feast, and two to bring in the stable boy)

Act 3

While the wedding guests watch the entertainment, Robin and his men, who are disguised, steal the gold from their pouches. When the Sheriff brings out the stable-boy, Robin gives the signal and he and his men swoop in to save him.

The guests hide under the tables until they realise that they've been robbed. The gold is found in the Sheriff's purse and when the wedding guests go after him, Robin and his men, Maid Marian and the stable-boy escape.

FRIAR TUCK
A cheerful man who likes his food and is always willing to help when someone is in need.

MAID MARIAN
A brave and adventurous young woman who cares more for the poor people than for the riches she was born with.

SHERIFF OF NOTTINGHAM
A vile and wicked man who uses his power to get what he wants, no matter who he hurts along the way.

STABLE-BOY
A courageous boy who risks his life to help Maid Marian.

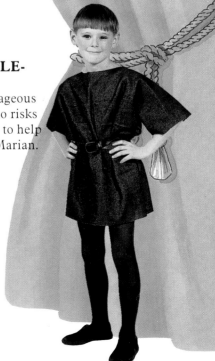

ROBIN HOOD AND HIS MEN

Robin Hood and his men wear tights, green tunics and special hats.

Will Scarlet has a rope attached to his belt.

Make the tunics like Friar Tuck's tunic (below), but shorter. Make the hats as shown.

ROBIN HOOD AND HIS MEN (IN DISGUISE)

Robin wears a long cape with a hood. He carries a basket of apples, and a whistle. Make a plain cape like the Sheriff's (on page 11) but weave the ribbon further down the cape to make a baggy hood. Will wears a long cape like Robin's and carries a recorder.

Little John wears a jester's hat and a brightly coloured tunic over his clothes. He carries three balls for juggling. Make the hat and tunic as shown.

FRIAR TUCK

Friar Tuck wears a long brown tunic tied at the waist with a rope. Make the tunic as shown. If you wish, you can also make a skull cap to add to the effect.

ROBIN HOOD'S HAT

1 To make the hat, cut out two triangles of felt a little longer than the length of your head.

2 Sew or glue with fabric glue along two edges.

3 Decorate Robin's hat with a feather.

LITTLE JOHN'S TUNIC AND JESTER'S HAT

1 To make the tunic, fold a long piece of material in half and cut a hole for the neck.

2 Sew ribbons at the waist for tying together and decorate with patches of bright fabric cut in the shape of diamonds.

3 To make the hat, cut two long triangles of felt. Sew or glue with fabric glue along the two sides and decorate it with bells and shapes cut out of coloured felt.

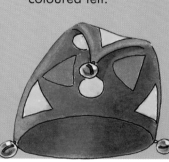

FRIAR TUCK'S TUNIC AND CAP

1 To make the tunic, fold a long piece of brown material in half and cut out a T-shape.

2 Sew or glue with fabric glue up the sides and along the bottom and top of the arms to form sleeves. Cut a hole for the neck.

3 To make the skull cap, cut a circle out of brown felt. Make a cut from the edge to the centre. Overlap the edges and glue together. Fix in place with hairgrips.

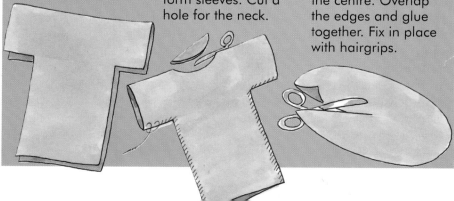

MAID MARIAN

In the first act, Maid Marian wears the same type of tunic, tights and hat as Robin Hood (on page 10).

In the last act, she wears a tall hat and a long dress with a scarf tied around her hips. She carries three bags of gold. Make the hat and the bags of gold as shown.

BAGS OF GOLD AND MAID MARIAN'S HAT

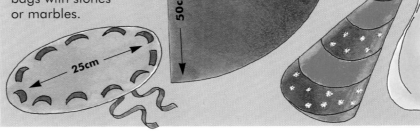

1 To make the bags of gold, cut three 25cm circles out of felt. Use a hole punch to make holes around the edge. Thread a ribbon through the holes pull it tight. Fill the bags with stones or marbles.

2 To make the hat, cut a large quarter-circle out of thin card.

3 Overlap the edges to form a cone and glue the edges together. Decorate with glitter. Staple or glue a piece of fabric to the top.

50cm

25cm

SHERIFF OF NOTTINGHAM

The sheriff wears trousers and a white shirt with a black cape and black boots or shoes. Make the cape as shown.

SHERIFF'S CAPE

1 To make the cape, take a large piece of dark fabric and cut small holes along the top edge.

2 Weave a ribbon through the openings and tie the ends in a bow at your neck.

3 Decorate the cape with shiny buttons that look like jewels.

WEDDING GUESTS

The girls wear dresses and hats similar to Maid Marian's (above). The boys wear trousers and white shirts with short capes. Each guest should have a money pouch tied to his or her waist.

Make the capes like the Sheriff's (above), but make them shorter and from light-coloured fabric. Make the money pouches like Maid Marian's bags of gold (above).

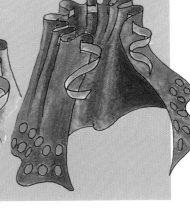

GUARDS

The guards wear red tights and white shirts with red tunics. Make the tunics like Little John's tunic (on page 10), and decorate the front with a large crown made with glitter.

STABLE-BOY

The stable-boy wears brown tights and a brown tunic. Make a tunic like Friar Tuck's (page 10), but shorter.

SCENERY

You will need to make two sets of flats so that one set can stand on each side of the stage. To make the flats, follow the instructions on page 6 and paint them to look like a forest.

CASTLE WALLS

Take two pieces of fabric, such as muslin or sheeting, large enough to cover the two flats. Paint a stone wall and castle windows on them. Staple the fabric to the back of the flats at the top only. This hangs down the back of the flats for the first two acts. For the last act, flip the fabric over to cover the forest scene and add the royal banners (see below).

ACTS ONE and TWO take place in Sherwood Forest.
• Make some flats, and lots of trees.

ACT THREE takes place in the castle
• Make some castle walls
• Place tables and chairs on the stage for the wedding guests.
• Have some rope at the side of the stage for Robin and his men to tie up the Sheriff and guards.

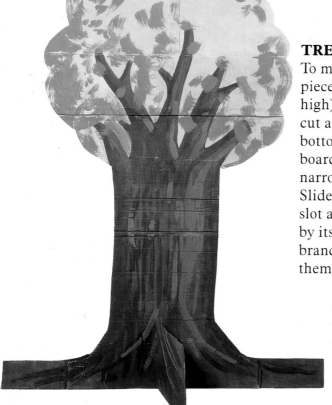

TREES

To make each tree, cut a large piece of cardboard (about 1.5m high) in the shape of a tree and cut a narrow 30cm slot from the bottom. Cut a base out of cardboard 60cm high, and cut a narrow 30cm slot from the top. Slide the base slot into the tree slot and your tree will stand up by itself. Paint on the bark, branches and leaves. Place them around the stage.

ROYAL BANNERS

To make the royal banners, use several pieces of lightweight fabric. Glue or sew a wide hem at the top and run a stick or broom handle through it. Decorate the banners with glitter in the shape of crowns. Attach string to either end of the stick and hang the banner to the top of the flats with drawing pins.

THE PLAY
ACT ONE

Sherwood Forest. Maid Marian, dressed like a boy, ENTERS, whistling. Robin Hood and his men are hiding behind the trees. When Marian gets to the middle of the stage, Robin Hood steps out and stops her.

Robin Hood: Fine day, wouldn't you say?

Marian: Yes. (*She tries to lower her voice.*) Yes. A very fine day.

She tries to continue on her way, but Robin stops her.

Robin: A fine day for walking in the forest?

Marian: (*trying to get by*) Yes, it is.

Robin: (*stopping her*) Could be very dangerous for a young boy like yourself. (*He puts his arm around her shoulder and looks around.*) You know, there are thieves in these woods.

Marian: (*excited*) What thieves? Robin Hood? Do you know him?

Robin: Indeed I do. He's a no-good, low-down, slimy-bellied thief.

Robin Hood's men laugh from behind the trees.

Marian: (*leaping back and putting her fists in the air*) You are a liar, sir, and I'll ask you to take back what you've said about Robin Hood.

Robin: (*laughing*) Oh, you'll fight me, will you?

Marian: (*keeping her fists up*) If I must.

Robin: But why? Everyone knows what a scoundrel he is.

Marian: That's not true. Everyone knows Robin Hood is heroic and brave. Now take it back or fight!

Robin's men come out from behind the trees to watch as she dances around Robin, challenging him to fight.

Robin: I think he means what he says.

Will: (*laughing*) He is trespassing you know. Maybe we ought to teach him a lesson.

The men all laugh with him, which makes Marian angry. She lunges at Robin, but he stops her by holding the top of her head. She swings wildly, but is unable to reach him.

John: (*laughing*) Do you need some help?

Robin: No, I think I can handle this one.

Marian grabs Robin's free hand and bites it. Robin yells and jerks both his hands away, pulling her hat off and revealing her hair.

John: Hey! He's not a boy at all, Robin.

Will: He's a girl!

Marian: (*looking at Robin, surprised*) Did he call you Robin? You are Robin Hood?

Robin: (*rubbing his hand*) I would shake your hand, but I'm afraid you'd bite it.

Marian: (*crossing her arms*) I'm sorry, but you really should have told me who you were.

Robin: (*putting his hands on his hips*) And who, pray tell, are you?

Marian: Maid Marian from Nottingham.

John: But why are you way out here?

Marian: I came looking for Robin. (*to Robin*) Please, I need your help.

Will:	*(suspiciously)* What kind of help?
Marian:	To save a young boy's life. A stable-boy. He helped me to escape from the Sheriff of Nottingham who was holding me prisoner and now the Sheriff is going to execute him.
Robin:	Why was the Sheriff holding you prisoner?
Marian:	*(she looks disgusted)* He wanted me to marry him.
Robin:	He's a very rich man.
Marian:	He's a vile and wicked man. He tried to tempt me with bags of gold.
Will:	Gold?
John:	Bags did you say?
Robin:	How many bags?
Marian:	Oh, three or four. I didn't pay much attention to his filthy money.
Robin:	But three bags of gold could feed a lot of poor people in Nottingham.
Marian:	Of course. I wasn't thinking. But I'm afraid I left it in my room.
Robin:	No matter. We'll get it back.
Marian:	But we don't have time. We have to save the stable-boy.
Robin:	We can do both. But first, you must go back to the Sheriff.
Marian:	Go back?
Robin:	And tell him you've been foolish.
Marian:	Never!
Robin:	And that you will gladly marry him tomorrow.
Marian:	*(angrily)* I thought you were going to help me.
Robin:	We are. *(He begins to lead her off-stage.)* All you have to do is... *(He whispers the rest in her ear.)*

Just before they EXIT, Marian claps her hands.

Marian:	Oh, Robin that's a splendid idea!
Robin:	*(to his men)* Come on then, there's work to do!

Robin's men follow Robin and Marian and EXIT.

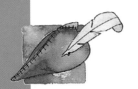

ACT TWO

Sherwood Forest. Friar Tuck is sitting in the centre of the stage, with rope tied around him. Some of Robin's men are guarding him. Robin Hood ENTERS, with Little John and Will Scarlet.

Will: We caught him snooping around on the path.

John: He wasn't exactly snooping.

Robin: What was he doing?

Will: Well, um...

Robin: Well?

John: He was singing.

Robin: (*laughing*) Singing? Was it so bad you had to tie the poor fellow up?

He walks over to Friar Tuck and pats him on the back. Tuck smiles.

Robin: Where might you be going, my jolly fellow?

Tuck: A long journey. A tiring journey.

Robin: Yes, you look like you've come a long way.

John: What's your name?

Tuck: Friar Tuck at your service. (*He tries to shake hands, but can't because of the ropes.*)

Will: (*to Robin and John*) He might be a spy!

Tuck:	*(licking his lips)* Would you, by any chance, have a small roast chicken?
John:	You mean a spy from the Sheriff of Nottingham?

Will nods his head and the three of them stare at Tuck.

Tuck:	A small sausage roll would do nicely.
Will:	He's a tricky fox, the Sheriff of Nottingham.
Tuck:	Or a small piece of apple pie.
Robin:	Are you hungry, Friar?
Tuck:	*(looking relieved)* Oh, yes!
Robin:	At our camp we have a delicious, tasty, juicy roast pig with a bright red apple in its mouth.

As Robin emphasises each word, the Friar licks his lips and rolls his eyes.

Tuck:	Oh my!
Robin:	Tell us, sir, where you're going this fine day, and the pig is all yours.
Tuck:	*(leaning towards Robin)* The apple too? *(Robin nods.)* That is easy, friend. I'm going to the castle of Nottingham.
Will:	I told you he was a spy.
John:	To see the Sheriff of Nottingham?
Tuck:	In a manner of speaking, yes.
Will:	*(menacingly, glaring at Tuck)* We have a message for the Sheriff of Nottingham.
Tuck:	I have a message for him too. *(He sticks out his tongue and blows a raspberry.)*
Robin:	Don't you like the Sheriff?
Tuck:	Of course not! He's the most cruel, heartless man on earth. And his banquets are tasteless. *(Yuk!)* I've had better food from a pig's trough.
John:	Then why are you going to the castle?
Tuck:	I have no choice. *(He shakes his head)* It's a sad day.
John:	What do you mean?
Tuck:	I've been ordered to sing for his wedding. I'd rather eat rats' tails than sing at his wedding.

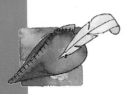

Will:	Why is that?
Tuck:	The scoundrel is forcing a beautiful young girl named Marian to marry him. (*He sighs.*) Such a shame. I love to sing, you see. (*He begins to warm up.*) La, la, la, la, la.
Robin:	Yes, indeed, but Friar, how would you like to stop this marriage and save an innocent boy as well?
Tuck:	Certainly. (*looking worried*) But will I still get to taste some of that roast pig?
Robin:	(*laughing*) Of course, and all the food you can carry with you. We'll tell you our plan on the way to camp.

Robin unties Friar Tuck, puts his arm around him and whispers the plan to him as everyone EXITS.

CURTAIN

ACT THREE

The Sheriff's castle. The wedding guests are sitting at tables and talking excitedly about the wedding. The Sheriff ENTERS and waves his arms to get their attention.

Sheriff: Welcome dear friends and thank you for coming to this most glorious occasion, my wedding day!

Everyone claps.

Sheriff: While you are waiting for the festivities to begin, I have arranged entertainment, thanks to our good Friar.

He motions for Tuck to come in, then EXITS. As the audience cheers, Tuck welcomes the entertainers, who are really Robin's men in disguise. John is a juggling jester and Will plays a flute. Robin is dressed like an old woman and he stands at the side of the stage. While the wedding guests watch John and Will juggle and play, the other members of Robin's band crawl behind the guests and take the money pouches that hang from the waist of each guest. When they have collected the pouches, the men meet Robin at the side of the stage and put the pouches into his basket. John and Will continue to entertain the guests.

Robin: Very good! Well done! Now get ready – here comes the sheriff.

They hide at the back of the crowd. The Sheriff ENTERS, dragging Marian behind him. Robin, Tuck, John and Will stand to one side, watching.

Sheriff: And now the moment you've been waiting for! It's time for the wedding to commence.

The guests cheer.

Sheriff: But wait. Wait. I have another surprise. *(calling to his guards)* Bring out the prisoner.

The guards ENTER dragging the stable-boy.

Sheriff: This ragged little urchin has committed a horrible crime. He stood in the way of true love.

Boy: I didn't!

Sheriff: Silence!

A guard puts his hand over the boy's mouth.

Sheriff: He kidnapped my bride-to-be and tried to take her away from me.

The guests gasp in surprise and begin to boo and hiss at the boy.

Sheriff: But luckily my beautiful bride was too quick-witted and she managed to escape his evil plot.

The guests clap politely and say 'Ahhh'.

Sheriff: So today you have two treats...

He kisses Marian's hand.

Sheriff: A wedding... *(He points to the stable-boy.)* ... and an execution!

The guests break out into loud cheering.

Sheriff: But first the wedding. My dear?

As he takes Marian by the arm, Robin Hood pulls off his headscarf and takes a whistle from his basket. When he blows the signal, his band of men run out yelling and the guests scream and hide under the tables. Marian and Tuck tie a rope around the Sheriff, so that his arms are tied but his legs are free. Little John and Will Scarlet tie the guards together in the same way and rescue the boy.

Guests:	Help, we're being robbed! Help!
Man:	Wait a minute. I've already been robbed. My bag is missing.
Guests:	*(all at once)* Mine too. And mine!
Marian:	Yes, and here's your gold. *(She holds up a bag of gold and points to the Sheriff.)* And here's your thief!

The wedding guests shout angrily and surround the Sheriff and his guards, forcing them to EXIT. The guests follow and EXIT, still shouting.

John:	Good work, Robin. Success! *(He slaps Robin on the back.)*
Marian:	And that's not all. *(She holds up the three bags of gold that the Sheriff gave her.)*
Robin:	The poor will eat well tonight!

They cheer and clap as they EXIT.

Tuck:	Do you think there will be a spare chicken or two? All this excitement has made me hungry again.

CURTAIN

JUNGLE BOOK
THE STORY

Before the first rehearsal, read through the script on your own so that you know the story. If you are acting a part, think about the character of the person you play and the best way of showing it.

Act 1

Bagheera the panther comes to see how Mowgli the man-cub is getting along in his lessons with Baloo the bear. Bagheera is impressed when Mowgli recites the Law of the Jungle, but gets very angry when he finds out that Mowgli has been talking to the monkey people.

Act 2

The monkey people kidnap Mowgli because they want him to be their leader. Shere Kahn the tiger warns Bagheera and Baloo that if he finds Mowgli first he'll have him as a tasty snack. Chil the Falcon tells Bagheera and Baloo that the monkey people have taken Mowgli to the Lost City. They decide to ask Kaa the Python for help.

MOWGLI
A bright and mischievous young boy who has been raised in the jungle and can talk to all of the animals.

BALOO
A lovable, but sometimes impatient brown bear who is Mowgli's teacher and best friend.

MONKEY PEOPLE
They are naughty and mischievous.

BAGHEERA
The gentle black panther who protects Mowgli from harm. He is usually very patient, but loses his temper when Mowgli does things that could get him into trouble.

CAST LIST

- ★ Mowgli
- ★ Baloo, a bear
- ★ Bagheera, a panther
- ★ Shere Kahn, a tiger
- ★ Chil, a falcon
- ★ Kaa, a python
- ★ Monkey people (as many as you like, with two speaking parts)
- ★ Cobras (as many as you like)

Act 3

The monkey people take Mowgli to the Lost City. Mowgli is tired and hungry when they arrive, but the monkeys are silly and do nothing but chatter and imitate their new leader. Mowgli gets tired of this and sets off to find his own food. Bagheera and Baloo meet Kaa the python at the Lost City and Kaa calls on his brother snakes, the cobras, to surround and protect Mowgli. The monkeys run away in fear and Bagheera and Baloo take Mowgli home.

KAA
The master of the snakes. When he speaks, he makes a hissing noise whenever he says the letter 'S'.

SHERE KAHN
A wicked tiger who is always trying to catch Mowgli on his own.

CHIL
A falcon who carries a message to Bagheera that helps to save Mowgli from the monkey people.

COBRAS
They hiss and sway from side to side, and are very menacing.

BAGHEERA

Bagheera wears a black leotard and black tights. He has a black tail and black ears. Follow the instructions below to make the ears. Make a tail as shown. Paint your face black and your nose, lips and eye-brows white. Draw on white whiskers.

BAGHEERA'S AND SHERE KAHN'S TAIL

1 To make a tail, fold a long strip of fabric down the middle and sew the two edges together.

2 Sew across one end of the strip. Turn inside out so that the stitches or glue are hidden.

3 Stuff it with cotton wool and attach it to the back of your leotard.

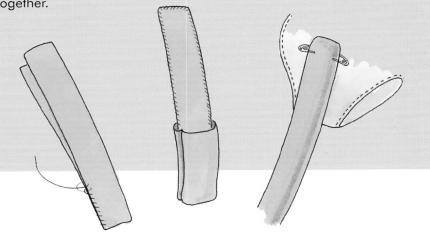

SHERE KAHN

Shere Kahn wears an orange or yellow leotard and tights and has a yellow tail and pointed ears.

Make the ears as shown. Follow the instructions above to make a tail.

Use theatrical face paints or make-up to outline your nose and mouth in black. Draw on black whiskers.

EARS

1 To make ears, fold a piece of stiff paper or fabric and cut an ear shape, so that the two pieces of the ear are joined at the tip.

2 Fold in 2.5cm at the bottom of each piece to make a tab and glue together.

3 Sew or glue the tabs to a hairband. Make another ear in the same way.

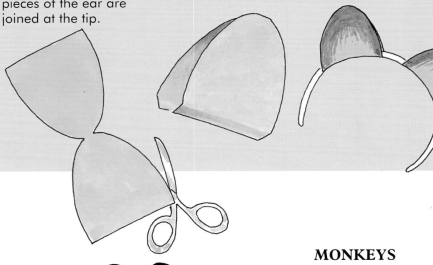

MOWGLI

All Mowgli wears is a pair of shorts. Cut around the bottom of each leg of a pair of old trousers. He also needs a banana to throw at Baloo. He should stand on a chair off-stage and throw the banana.

MONKEYS

The monkeys wear brown leotards and tights, and have brown tails and ears. Make the ears and tails as shown above. Make the ears rounded instead of pointed.

BALOO

Baloo wears a costume that makes him look big around the middle, and has brown ears. Make parts of the costume as shown. Make a matching brown tunic using the instructions for Friar Tuck's tunic on page 10. Make rounded ears as shown on page 24.

Make a matching brown tunic using the instructions for Friar Tuck's tunic on page 10. Make rounded ears as shown on page 24.

BALOO'S TROUSERS

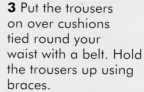

1 Cut two extra-large trouser shapes out of brown material.

2 Sew or glue with fabric glue along the sides and up the inside leg seam. Turn inside out.

3 Put the trousers on over cushions tied round your waist with a belt. Hold the trousers up using braces.

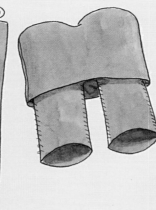

CHIL

Chil wears dark tights with a dark long-sleeved t-shirt or sweatshirt covered in feathers. He also needs a yellow beak. Make the feathers and the beak as shown.

CHIL'S FEATHERS AND BEAK

1 To make feathers, cut strips of brown and black crêpe paper and attach them to the shirt, sewing the middle of each strip to the top of the sleeve.

2 To make the beak, cut two beak shapes from yellow card and sticky-tape the two longer edges together, leaving the end open to fit over your nose.

3 Punch holes at the sides and thread a piece of elastic through the holes. Tie knots in the ends of the elastic to hold the nose in place.

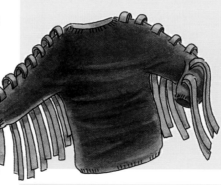
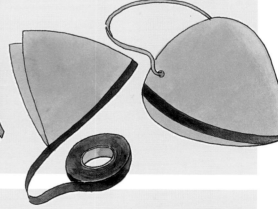

KAA AND THE COBRAS

All the snakes wear black leotards and tights. Their faces are painted to look like snakes. Make Kaa look different by using other colours, such as a purple base and blue scales.

COBRA MAKE-UP

1 Paint your face and arms with yellow face paint. Use only proper theatrical face paints or make-up.

2 Paint deep green stripes or scales on your face and arms.

3 Outline mouth and eyes with black. Add green and gold glitter paint to the scales.

SCENERY

Make three flats following the directions on page 6. Paint the flats light green at the bottom and blue at the top. Let them dry completely. Paint tropical trees and vines all over them.

ACTS ONE and TWO
are set in the jungle.
- Make some flats.
- Make plenty of trees and place them around the stage.

ACT THREE
is set in the Lost City.
- Make two stone columns.
- Make some city walls and vines to drape over them.

TREES

To make each tree, cut a large piece of cardboard (about 1.5m high) in the shape of a palm tree and cut a narrow 30cm slot from the bottom. Cut a base 60cm high, and cut a narrow 30cm slot from the top. Slide the base slot into the tree slot and your tree will stand up by itself. Paint on the bark, branches and leaves.

CITY WALLS

Stack and glue several cardboard boxes together to make a wall, and paint them to look like ruins. Cover them with vines (see below) and place them at the back of the stage. You should be able to see the jungle flats above them, as the Lost City is in the heart of the jungle.

COLUMNS

To make a stone column, roll a sheet of corrugated cardboard into a tube and glue the edges together. Make another tube in the same way and attach the two together using tape. Find two small cardboard boxes of the same size. Stand the cardboard tube in the middle of each box and trace around the tube. Cut out the circles and fit the top and bottom of the column into the circles. Hold in place with masking tape and paint the column and boxes grey. When the paint is dry, wrap vines around them and place them around the stage.

VINES

The Lost City is overrun with vines. These are easy to make with green gardening twine. Cut out leaves from green paper and staple them on to the twine. Drape the vines all over the stage and hang them from the ceiling if possible.

THE PLAY
ACT ONE

In the jungle. Baloo is searching among the trees, looking up into the branches for Mowgli.

Baloo: Mowgli. Your lessons are not over. Come down here at once.

Mowgli: *(off-stage)* No. I won't.

Bagheera ENTERS.

Bagheera: Hello, Baloo. How is Mowgli doing with his lessons?

Baloo: *(shrugging)* His climbing is improving.

A banana hits Baloo on the back.

Baloo: Ouch! But his temper needs improving.

Bagheera: What did you do this time?

Baloo: Me? *(He crosses his arms.)* I did nothing.

Bagheera: Nothing?

Baloo: Well, I yelled a little. *(Bagheera shakes his head.)* All right. I yelled a lot, but he deserved it.

Bagheera: He's only a little man-cub, Baloo.

Baloo: I know, Bagheera. That's why I have to teach him so much. He doesn't have claws or teeth like we do and he can't run as fast as you can.

Bagheera: Is he a good student?

Baloo: The best. The best student I've ever had.

Bagheera: *(proudly)* I knew it.

Bagheera calls up into the trees.

Bagheera: Mowgli! Come down. I want to hear you recite the Laws of the Jungle.

Mowgli:	(*off-stage*) No!
Bagheera:	Baloo says you can recite the law without taking a breath.
Mowgli:	(*off-stage*) I can.
Bagheera:	So show me. I don't believe it.

Mowgli ENTERS. He puts his nose in the air when he passes Baloo.

Mowgli:	I'll come out for you, Bagheera. But not for rotten old Baloo.
Baloo:	Hmmph. They never appreciate the teacher.
Bagheera:	Now then, Mowgli. What do you say when you come upon a hive of wild bees?
Mowgli:	I am very polite and I say, 'Excuse me pl-e-e-z b-e-e-z, I will climb other tr-e-e-z'.
Baloo:	(*proudly*) I taught him that in one hour. (*He makes a sweeping bow.*) Pl-e-e-e-ease be-e-ees!
Bagheera:	Ssshh, Baloo! (*to Mowgli*) And when you want to swim?
Mowgli:	I give a warning, 'We are cousins, gentle snakes-s-s. May I swim, please, in these lakes?'.
Bagheera:	Well done little man-cub!
Mowgli:	(*bragging*) I know every language in the jungle now.
Baloo:	(*pouting*) I did the hard work. Do you know how hard it is to get masterwords from the elephants? They always pretend to forget.
Bagheera:	(*ignoring Baloo*) So, little Mowgli, why did big, bad Baloo yell at you?
Mowgli:	I learned a language all by myself.
Bagheera:	(*to Baloo*) Shame on you Baloo, for being jealous of our little man-cub.
Baloo:	But Bagheera...
Bagheera:	(*putting his arm around Mowgli*) You should be proud. (*gently to Mowgli*) What language did you learn, Mowgli?

Mowgli: The language of the monkey people.

Bagheera: (*shouting angrily*) WHAT?! The monkey people? Never! Never speak of the monkey people.

Mowgli hides behind Baloo.

Baloo: (*to Bagheera*) I tried to tell him.

Mowgli: But Bagheera, they stand on their feet like me.

Bagheera: (*shouting*) They are apes without law.

Baloo: I told him that too.

Mowgli: They said I was a blood brother except that I don't have a tail.

Baloo: (*shaking his head*) He won't listen, Bagheera.

Bagheera: (*shouting*) They are the outcasts of the jungle!

Mowgli: (*crossing his arms and shouting back*) They don't yell at me! (*bragging*) And they told me I could be their leader.

Bagheera: They have no leader. They are liars.

Baloo: We're only trying to protect you. We're your friends.

Bagheera: The monkey people are forbidden. Do you understand?

Mowgli: (*shrugging*) Yes. I guess so.

Bagheera: Good. Now it's time for our daily nap in the sun.

Mowgli: Do you forgive me, Bagheera?

Bagheera: Of course I do. Besides, it's Baloo's fault. He should have told you about them.

Bagheera and Mowgli EXIT. Baloo follows.

Baloo: Me? How was I supposed to know he'd play with dirt? Monkey people.... P-tooie. (*He makes a spitting noise as he EXITS.*)

ACT TWO

The jungle. The stage is empty. Two monkeys ENTER from behind the trees and look around.

Monkey 1:   Ssshh! Keep watch.

Monkey 2:   Keep watch for what?

Monkey 1:   Make sure no one sees.

Monkey 2:   Sees what?

Monkey 1:   Where we take the man-cub.

Monkey 2:   Oh! Did we take the man-cub?

Monkey 1:   Of course we did. *(he snaps his fingers)* Just like that. Swooped down from the trees. Bagheera and Baloo slept right through it.

Monkey 2:   Tell me again why we want the man-cub.

Monkey 1:   What man-cub?

Monkey 2:   The one we just kidnapped.

Monkey 1:   Oh, I forgot.

Monkey 2:   Forgot what?

Monkey 1:   The man-cub.

Monkey 2:   Why do we need a man-cub?

Monkey 1:   To be our leader.

Monkey 2:   To lead us where?

Monkey 1:   I don't know. Home?

Monkey 2:   OK. Let's go home.

The monkeys EXIT RIGHT and Bagheera and Baloo ENTER LEFT.

Bagheera: If you had warned him, none of this would have happened.

Baloo   Well, if you hadn't been snoring so loudly, I would have heard them take him.

Shere Kahn ENTERS.

Shere Kahn: Lost something?

Baloo: Nothing. Mind your own business, Shere Khan.

Shere Kahn:	Oh, but it is my business. The boy rightfully belongs to me. I found him first.
Bagheera:	He's one of us now.
Shere Kahn:	Only because you stole him from me.
Baloo:	Mowgli wasn't safe with you, and you know it. He's only a very small man-cub.
Shere Kahn:	And a very tasty morsel if I find him first. *He EXITS, snarling.*
Bagheera:	We need help, Baloo. We must find Mowgli before Shere Kahn does.

Chil the Falcon ENTERS flapping his wings.

Chil:	News! I have news!
Bagheera:	What is it? What have you seen?
Chil:	I saw the monkey people taking Mowgli.
Baloo:	Where?
Chil:	I couldn't follow them for long, but Mowgli spoke to me in my own language and has sent you a message.
Baloo:	*(proudly)* See? I have taught him well. It took me only...
Bagheera:	Will you be quiet, Baloo? *(to Chil)* What's the message?
Chil:	The Lost City. That's where they've taken Mowgli.
Baloo:	The Lost City? That's very dangerous. What now, Bagheera?
Bagheera:	*(thinking)* We must speak to Kaa.
Baloo:	The python? I don't like him. He gives hugs that squeeze the life out of you.
Bagheera:	It's our only hope. Kaa and his cobras are the only creatures in the jungle that the monkey people fear.
Baloo:	All right. But you do all the talking. And no hugs!

They EXIT.

CURTAIN

ACT THREE

The Lost City. Mowgli ENTERS surrounded by several monkeys. The monkeys chatter and make monkey noises.

Monkey 1:   Welcome to your new home, oh leader of the monkey people.

Mowgli: *(stamping his feet)* But I told you, I'm not your leader.

The monkeys copy everything he does.

Monkeys: *(stamping their feet)* I'm not your leader. *(They giggle.)*

Mowgli: *(shaking his fist)* I want to go home!

Monkeys: *(shaking their fists)* I want to go home! *(They giggle.)*

Mowgli sits down in frustration and puts his head in his hands. One by one the monkeys sit next to him in a straight line, and copy him.

Mowgli: I'm tired

Monkeys: I'm tired. I'm tired.

Mowgli: And I'm hungry.

Monkeys: I'm hungry. I'm hungry.

Mowgli: *(jumping up and putting his hands on his hips)* If you aren't going to give me food, then I'm going to hunt for it myself.

The monkeys jump up and leap around, chattering and making monkey noises.

Monkeys: A hunt! A hunt! We're going on a hunt.

Mowgli starts to leave and they fall in line behind him. He stops and puts his hand up to stop them.

Mowgli: No, you stay.

Monkeys: You stay! You stay!

Mowgli takes a few more steps and they follow him. He stops again.

Mowgli: Don't follow me!

Monkeys: Follow me! Follow me!

Mowgli EXITS RIGHT and the monkeys follow him chanting.

Monkeys: Follow the leader! Follow the leader!

Bagheera and Baloo ENTER LEFT.

Baloo: I don't like it here. Can't we look somewhere else?

Bagheera: Sssh! *(whispering)* Kaa. Where are you?

Baloo: Maybe he's changed his mind.

Kaa ENTERS RIGHT.

Kaa: Who speaks-s-s-s my name?

Bagheera: It is I, Bagheera.

Baloo: Did you bring your friends?

Kaa: Didn't I promise-s-s-s?

Bagheera: Will they help?

Kaa: Of course-s-s-s.

Baloo: Then what are we waiting for? Call him, Bagheera.

Bagheera: *(calling)* Mowgli! Little man-cub!

Mowgli ENTERS RIGHT with the monkeys close behind.

Mowgli: Who's there? Who's calling?

Bagheera: Stand very still little Mowgli, and don't forget your lessons.

Monkey 1:   Our leader! Someone is trying to take our leader.

Two of the monkeys take Mowgli's arms to hold him.

Monkey 2:   (*pointing*) Look! Look over there!

Monkey 1:   The poison people!

The cobras ENTER on their knees, swaying their heads from side to side and hissing. The monkeys scream and EXIT, all going in different directions.

Mowgli: We are cousins, gentle snakes-s-s-s. May I offer many thanks!

The snakes stop and sway from side to side while Mowgli runs over and gives Bagheera and Baloo a hug.

Mowgli: I knew you'd come!

Bagheera: Don't you have something else to say?

Mowgli: (**turning to Kaa and bowing**) Many thanks-s-s-s, cousin.

Kaa: C-c-c-ertainly. If you'll excuse me I have s-s-s-upper to catch.

He EXITS. Bagheera, Baloo and Mowgli walk to centre stage.

Bagheera: You remembered your lessons well.

Baloo: Even better than big, old Baloo. *(He pats his tummy.)*

As they EXIT, Mowgli chatters like a monkey.

Mowgli: Big old Baloo! Big old Baloo!

Baloo: That's not funny, Mowgli. Stop it.

Mowgli: Stop it! Stop it!

They all EXIT.

CURTAIN

Before the first rehearsal, read through the script on your own so that you know the story. If you are acting a part, think about the character of the person you play and the best way of showing it.

Act 1

Captain Hook is an evil pirate, and the enemy of Peter Pan. The only thing he's afraid of is the crocodile that bit off his hand. Hook wants to capture Peter Pan, but his plans are not going well. He's in a very bad mood and he takes it out on his crew.

Smee, his assistant, suggests that they lure Peter to their ship, the Jolly Roger, by kidnapping his friends, Wendy, John, Michael and the Lost Boys. Hook likes that idea and they go below deck to make their plans.

JOHN
Wendy's brother. Sometimes he is boastful about what he knows about life beyond Neverland.

SMEE
Hook's long-suffering assistant.

CAPTAIN HOOK
A bad-tempered bully of a pirate who is feared by everyone.

MICHAEL
Wendy's youngest brother. He likes to copy his big brother, but he is easily frightened.

CAST LIST

- ★ Captain Hook
- ★ Smee
- ★ Peter Pan
- ★ Wendy
- ★ John
- ★ Michael

- ★ Tootles, a Lost Boy
- ★ Nibs, a Lost Boy
- ★ Slightly, a Lost Boy
- ★ Flint, a pirate
- ★ Billy Blade, a pirate
- ★ Pirates – you need four in addition to Flint and Billy

PETER PAN
A bold and fearless boy who enjoys having adventures.

Act 2

Hook and his pirates have captured Wendy, John, Michael and the Lost Boys. Hook tries to talk the boys into becoming pirates. When they refuse, he orders them to walk the plank while Wendy watches. Wendy gives a farewell speech, but before the boys walk the plank, Hook hears the sound of ticking. He knows it is the crocodile that bit off his hand, because it also swallowed a clock and ticks wherever it goes. Peter Pan arrives and Hook promises to free his prisoners if Peter can get rid of the crocodile. Hook does not realise the ticking is coming from a tape recorder and gives up his ship as well as his prisoners. Wendy and the boys are saved.

TOOTLES
The least brave of the Lost Boys, but kind and sweet-natured.

NIBS
A cheerful and adventurous Lost Boy.

BILLY BLADE, AND FLINT
Two young pirates, who are eager to please, but are terrified of Captain Hook.

WENDY
A kind and brave girl who takes pride in playing mother to the Lost Boys.

SLIGHTLY
The most conceited of the Lost Boys.

CAPTAIN HOOK

Hook wears a long black coat or waistcoat, a white ruffled shirt, and trousers. He has big silver buckles on his shoes. He also needs a sabre and a hook for his hand.

Sew large gold buttons down the front of the coat and sew gold trim and buttons on the cuffs. Make a hook as shown, and a sabre as shown below.

CAPTAIN'S HOOK

1 Bend the hook of a wire coat hanger into a loop, so there is no sharp end. Then bend the rest of the hanger into the shape of a hook.

2 Cover the hook with layers of foil. Push it through the bottom of a large plastic cup.

3 Paint the cup black. When the paint is dry, slip the cup over your hand and hold the hook in place.

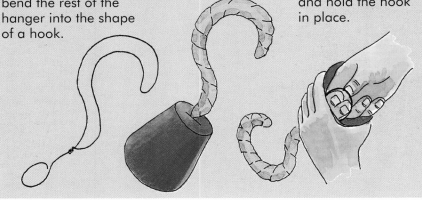

SMEE

Smee wears old trousers cut off in a jagged shape below the knee, and a white shirt or vest. He wears a sash around his waist and an eyepatch. Make the eyepatch as shown.

SMEE'S EYEPATCH

1 To make the eyepatch, cut an oval shape out of black felt or cardboard.

2 Make a hole in each side with a hole punch or a thick needle.

3 Thread elastic through the holes and tie it firmly around your head.

PIRATES

The pirates wear trousers like Smee's, t-shirts, and sashes around their waists. They have gold earrings, eyepatches and sabres. Follow the instructions, and make the sabres as shown. Billy also needs an alarm clock and a bundle of clothes to hold.

A PIRATE'S SABRE

1 To make a sabre, cut a sabre shape out of stiff cardboard.

2 Paint the handle and leave to dry.

3 Cover the blade section with silver foil and tuck the sabre into your belt or sash.

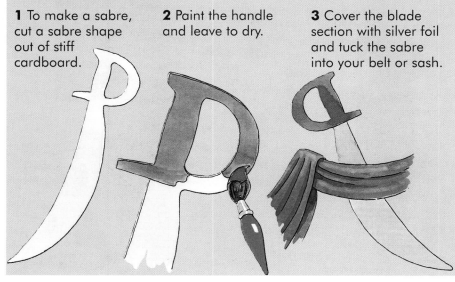

JOHN AND MICHAEL

Both John and Michael wear pyjamas. Michael carries a teddy bear, and John wears a top hat. Make the top hat as shown.

JOHN'S TOP HAT

1 Measure a sheet of black paper to fit around your head with a little to spare. Roll it so that the ends overlap and glue them together. Cut slits 2.5cm deep around the bottom and fold them out.

2 Place the other end of the tube on a sheet of black paper and trace around it. Draw another circle 7.5cm wider around it. Cut out the circle and the centre to create a ring.

3 Place the ring over the tube and glue the flaps to the underside of the ring.

THE LOST BOYS

The Lost Boys wear coloured t-shirts and trousers covered in leaves and patches of fake fur. Their faces and hair are streaked with brown and green. Make their costumes as shown.

THE LOST BOYS

1 Cut leaves out of different colours of paper or cloth and sew or glue them to the t-shirts and trousers.

2 Using theatrical face paints or make-up, smear green, brown and black streaks across your face.

3 Use hair spray or gel to make your hair stand up, and use spray cans of special hair colour to spray it brown and green.

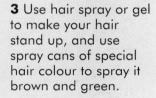

PETER PAN

Peter Pan wears green trousers and a green tunic cut off in a jagged shape around the neckline and bottom edge. Use face paint or make-up to make his eyebrows and lips green. Put glitter and green hair colour in his hair. He carries a small dagger tucked into a belt. Make a dagger using stiff cardboard. Paint the handle black and the blade silver or cover the blade with silver foil.

WENDY

Wendy wears a nightgown and a ribbon in her hair.

ACTS ONE AND TWO

The play takes place on the pirate ship, the Jolly Roger.
- Make a backdrop for the sky.
- Make a large sail and place it in the centre of the stage.
- Make three or four treasure chests.
- Put piles of rope around the deck and use in Act Two to tie up the Lost Boys, John and Michael.

SAILS

Paint a white skull and crossbones on a black square of fabric or an old sheet. You may need to use several coats of paint! Take two broomsticks or thin pieces of wood measuring 1m and 1.5m in length. Tie them together at one end so they make a right-angle. Staple or tack the painted sail along the shorter length of wood. Use the longer length as the mast.

Fill a bucket with sand or soil and push the mast into it. You can decorate the bucket to look like a barrel.

BACKDROP

Hang a sheet or curtain, preferably light blue so that it looks like the sky, at the back of the stage. Cut out white seagull shapes and pin them to the curtain or sheet.

SPLASH! SIGN

Whenever someone is thrown off the ship, one of the stage crew has to hold this sign out from off-stage. Make two signs, one smaller than the other, by cutting out rectangles from stiff card. Write SPLASH! on each one in large letters. Tape each card to a broomstick.

PLANK

For the plank you will need a long piece of wood. When Hook calls for it, the pirates go off-stage to fetch it, bring it on, and place it at the side of the stage, leading off-stage.

SOUND EFFECTS

TICKING CLOCK

Using a tape recorder, tape the sound of a ticking clock. When the script calls for it, one of the stage crew switches on the tape. When the ticking represents the crocodile, start quietly and gradually turn the volume up, so that it seems as if the crocodile is approaching.

TREASURE CHESTS

Paint empty cardboard boxes brown and decorate them with black paint. To make the handles, punch two holes on either side of the box and thread short pieces of rope through them. Tie knots in the ends of the rope on the inside. Fill the boxes with crumpled newspaper and on top place jewellery, cardboard crowns, pieces of rich-looking fabric, candlesticks, and anything else that looks like treasure.

THE PLAY
ACT ONE

Captain Hook is pacing back and forth on deck, while Smee follows behind him. The other pirates sit on deck waiting for their orders.

Hook: A surprise attack! That's what we need to capture that wretched boy.

Flint: But, Captain Hook, we've tried that before.

Hook: *(glaring at Flint)* You dare to disagree with me?

Flint: *(he gulps)* Yes, sir.

Hook: Very brave. What's your name?

Flint: Mad Dog Flint, sir

Hook: Throw him overboard.

Several pirates get up and throw Flint off-stage. The large SPLASH! sign appears from off-stage.

Smee: Maybe we could invite the Lost Boys on board the Jolly Roger to trick Peter Pan.

Hook grabs Smee's shirt and pulls him close, nose to nose.

Hook: And how would we do that?

Smee: *(nervously)* Invite them to tea? For a friendly chat?

Hook: *(shouting)* A friendly chat?

Smee: Yes, sir. Children love stories. You could tell them one of your stories.

Hook: Children may love stories, you simpleton, *(shouting)* but they don't love me.

Smee: But, sir...

Hook	Children hate me. My own men hate me. (*He turns to the other pirates.*) Don't you?
Pirates:	(*nodding in agreement and all speaking at once*) Aye aye, Captain. Yes, sir. That we do, sir.
Hook:	My own mother would hate me, if I had one.
Smee:	I think a mother would be very nice to have around. The Lost Boys have found a mother. Why don't we kidnap her for ourselves?
Hook:	(*shouting*) I don't want one! Pirates don't need mothers! (*He points to the other pirates.*) How many of you low-life idiots want a mother on board the Jolly Roger?
Pirate 1:	Well, it would be nice to be tucked in at night.
Pirate 2:	This ship hasn't been scrubbed in years.
Pirate 3:	Would she make apple tarts? With cinnamon on top? And crumbly, buttery pastry?
Hook:	(*scornfully*) You want to know what it would be like to have a mother around here?
Pirates:	(*nodding eagerly*) Aye, Captain. Aye, sir. Tell us.
Hook:	She'd tuck you in all right. (*He wraps his arm tightly around Pirate 1.*) So tight you couldn't go anywhere out of her sight.
Pirate 1:	Even when it was time for plundering?
Hook:	Especially then. (*He points to Pirate 2.*) And she'd have you scrubbing the decks and ironing the sails, and she'd expect you to clean yourself up for every meal.
Pirate 2:	You mean (*he gulps*) take a bath?
Hook:	Yes. And you'd have to wash behind your ears.

The pirates cover their ears to protect them.

Pirate 3:	What about the apple tarts?
Hook:	She might bake one.

The pirates sigh happily and rub their stomachs.

Hook:	But she wouldn't let you have any until she'd stuffed you with spinach and Brussels sprouts.
Pirates:	Eee-yuck. *(They make spitting noises.)*
Hook:	*(to the three pirates)* So do you still want a mother on board?
Pirates:	No sir, Captain Hook.
Hook:	Good. Throw them overboard.

The other pirates throw the three that were speaking off-stage. The SPLASH! sign is held up three times. Hook goes back to pacing up and down the deck.

Hook:	A surprise attack! That's what we need.
Smee:	We could kidnap the Lost Boys while Peter Pan is away.
Hook:	*(polishing his hook)* Kidnap. Yes. I like that.
Smee:	When Peter Pan comes back, he'll come looking for them.
Hook:	And we'll be ready.
Smee:	Aye aye, Captain.
Hook:	Hmmm. I think that might work.

(SOUND) The sound of a ticking clock can be heard.

Hook:	What's that sound?
Smee:	What sound Captain?
Hook:	*(terrified)* That ticking sound! Find it, Smee. Find it.

Hook hides behind one of the treasure chests, shaking with fear, while Smee looks over the side of the ship.

Smee: I don't see anything, Captain.

Hook: He's out there I tell you. Find him!

Smee crosses to the other side of the stage and looks out.

Smee: Seems to be coming from... (*He turns and walks back to the pirates, and stops in front of one pirate who is clutching a bundle to his chest.*) ... here! What do you have in that bundle, matey?

Billy: Just my belongings, sir, and an alarm clock. (*He hands the clock to Smee.*)

Smee: All's well, Captain. It's only young Billy Blade here. Brought his alarm clock with him.

Hook comes out from hiding, looking furious. Smee holds up the clock.

Hook: An alarm clock? (*shouting*) An alarm clock? On my ship? No one is allowed on my ship with an alarm clock. Throw it overboard.

Smee: Aye aye, Captain. (*He tosses the clock over the side.*)

The smaller SPLASH! sign appears from off-stage.

Billy: (*to Hook*) Sorry, Captain. I'm new at pirating, see? I was afraid I'd oversleep.

Hook: Very commendable. Throw him overboard.

Smee: Aye aye, Captain.

The last pirate throws him overboard. The large SPLASH! sign appears from off-stage.

Hook: Follow me below deck, Smee. It's time to plan a surprise attack.

Smee: Aye aye, Captain Hook. Come along men!

He stops when he realises that there is only one pirate left.

Smee: It will have to be a small attack, sir.

They EXIT.

ACT TWO

John, Michael and the Lost Boys are tied up on the deck of the Jolly Roger. They are guarded by Smee and the last pirate.

Michael: John, is he as terrible as they say?

John: *(nodding)* The worst of all the pirates.

Michael: *(gulping)* Where is he?

Nibs: Down below, sharpening his hook, I guess.

Michael: W-w-why does he have a hook?

Tootles: *(proudly)* Peter fed his hand to a crocodile.

Nibs: And the crocodile liked the taste so much he comes searching every day for a bigger chunk of Captain Hook.

Tootles: *(shaking his head)* But Hook escapes every time...

Slightly: ... because the crocodile swallowed a clock and every time Hook hears a tick-tock, tick-tock, he runs like the coward that he is.

Boys: *(together)* Tick-tock, tick-tock!

Hook ENTERS and points his hook at the boys.

Hook: Stop this at once or I'll run you through.

The boys stop.

Hook: *(to Smee)* Any sign of Peter Pan?

Smee: Not yet, Captain.

Hook: *(to the boys)* Now then, mateys. Today you will walk the plank. But I've decided to be generous. I happen to have some vacancies, so who wants to be a pirate?

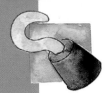

Tootles:	I don't think my mother would like me to be a pirate.
Boys:	*(together)* Me neither. Nor me.
Hook:	Quiet, you scugs. *(he points to John)* You boy. Wouldn't you like to be a pirate, my hearty?
John:	Could I choose my own name? Like Red-handed Jack?
Hook:	Aye. Any name you choose, if you join.
Michael:	What would you call me?
Hook:	Blackbeard Joe.
Michael:	What do you think, John?
John:	What would we have to do?
Hook:	You'd have to swear, 'Down with the King'.
John:	*(crossing his arms)* Then I refuse.
Michael:	*(doing the same)* I refuse too.
Boys:	*(together)* Me too. I refuse. And I refuse.
Hook:	*(angry)* So be it. Bring up their mother.

Smee EXITS.

Hook:	Prepare the plank.

*The pirate fetches the plank from off-stage and places it in position.
Smee* ENTERS *with Wendy.*

Hook:	So, my beauty. You are to watch your children walk the plank.
Wendy:	May I have a few last words?
Hook:	Of course. Silence! The mother wants to speak her last words to her children.
Wendy:	I give you this message as if it were from your own mothers.
Boys:	*(whispering together)* Our own mothers!
Wendy:	And this is the message. We hope our sons walk the plank like true gentlemen.
Tootles:	I'm going to walk the plank like a true gentleman.
Others:	*(together)* Me too! I'm going to walk the plank like a true gentleman. *(They cheer.)*
Hook:	Silence! Tie her up, Smee.

Smee starts to tie Wendy up. (SOUND) *The sound of ticking can be heard.*

Hook:	*(frightened)* Ticking. I hear ticking.

The ticking gets louder. One by one the boys join in a chant.

Boys:	Tick-tock here comes the croc.
	Tick-tock here comes the croc.
Hook:	*(cowering behind Smee)* Make it stop, Smee! *(He cries.)* I want my mummy!

Peter Pan ENTERS and points at Hook.

Peter Pan:	You don't have a mother, you villain. You've stolen one that doesn't belong to you.
Wendy & **The boys:**	Peter Pan! *(They cheer.)*
Hook:	*(begging on his knees)* You can have her back, Pan, and the boys. You can even have my ship, if you'll just get rid of that croc.
Peter Pan:	It's a deal.
Hook:	*(crying)* Oh, thank you.

Hook covers his head and cowers and Smee and the pirate stand over him to protect him, with their backs to Peter Pan. Peter Pan fetches the tape recorder from off-stage. He turns it off, then hides it behind one of the Lost Boys. Hook, Smee and the pirate don't see this. The ticking stops. Wendy and the boys giggle.

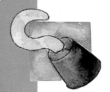

Hook:	Is it gone?
Peter Pan:	It's gone. Now release your prisoners.
Hook:	*(standing up)* Release them, Smee.

Smee unties Wendy and the Lost Boys.

Peter Pan:	And now, Hook, you and your crew into the rowing boat.
Hook:	Surely you can't expect me to really give you my ship. I was in a state of panic. I wasn't serious.
Peter Pan:	*(Pointing his sword at Hook)* Going back on your word, Hook?
Hook:	Smee, what are you waiting for? Tell the men to attack.
Smee:	But sir. You threw them all overboard.

Peter Pan and the boys surround Hook.

Peter Pan:	Into the rowing boat, Hook. Now!

The Lost Boys raise their fists, and Peter Pan chases Hook, Smee and the pirate off-stage.

Hook:	You haven't seen the last of me, Pan.
All:	Hurrah!

Peter Pan returns to the centre of the stage.

Wendy:	We must hurry home children, or we'll be late for supper.
Nibs:	What are we having?
Wendy:	Apple tarts.
Tootles:	With cinnamon on top?
Wendy:	*(nodding)* And crumbly, buttery pastry.
Boys:	*(together)* Tick-tock, tick-tock, saved by the croc!
	Tick-tock, tick-tock, saved by the croc!

They continue to chant as they all EXIT.

CURTAIN